SPRING

A collection of
Poems, Songs and Stories
for young children

**Wynstones
Press**

Published by
Wynstones Press
Ruskin Glass Centre
Wollaston Road
Stourbridge
West Midlands DY8 4HE.
England.
Telephone: +44 (0) 1384 399455
Email: info@wynstonespress.com

First Published 1978 by Wynstones Press
Second edition with music 1983
Fully revised third edition 1999. Reprinted 2005.

Editors: Jennifer Aulie and Margret Meyerkort

Cover illustration of 'The Fisherman' by David Newbatt

Typeset by Wynstones Press.
Printed in the EU by Cambrian Printers.

British Library CIP data available.

ISBN 0 946206 46 5

Spring

This is one in a series of 6 books:
Spring, Summer, Autumn, Winter, Spindrift and Gateways.

The four seasonal books comprise a wide selection of poems, songs and stories appropriate to the time of year, including much material for the celebration of festivals.

Spindrift contains verses and songs describing the world of daily work and practical life, together with a selection of stories from around the world.

Gateways comprises verses and songs for the Morning time, the Evening time and to accompany a variety of traditional Fairytales, together with poems, songs and stories for the celebration of Birthdays.

Warmest thanks to all who have contributed to and supported this work: parents, teachers and friends from Steiner Waldorf Schools in Australia, Britain, Canada, Eire, Estonia, New Zealand, Norway, South Africa and the United States. Grateful thanks also to publishers who have permitted the use of copyright material, acknowledgements for which are at the end of the volume.

INDEX

Indexes of first lines
POEMS

SONGS

Index of titles
STORIES

The Value of Music in the Life of the Young Child

Free Play in a Waldorf Kindergarten. It is a winter morning: the twenty children are busy with their work. The youngest, three- and four-year-olds, are helping the teacher chop apples for snack; some five-year-old girls are taking care of their "children" in the doll corner; next to them are a group of five-year-old boys and girls who are sitting at a round table polishing stones, grating chestnuts and chatting together. In the centre of the room an observant and energetic four-year-old boy is directing the six-year-olds in the construction of a snowplough: tables are stacked on each other, chairs turned upside down and leaned against the tables for the front part of the plough. A large basket of chestnuts is balanced on top of the plough. The chestnuts are grit and salt, to be scattered later on the ploughed streets. The room is small and the noise level is moderately high.

Underneath the windows, on the carpet where the children have a free space to build up scenes and play with standing puppets and animals, a six-year-old girl sits, absorbed in her work. She has laid out a forest of pine cones, which stands on the banks of a river of blue cloth. Stepping stones allow the poor shepherd boy, who lives at the edge of the forest, to cross the river and wind his way to the castle gates nearby . . . The princess, leaning out of her tower, sees him coming and calls down to him . . .

As she lays out the scene, the girl accompanies her actions with narrative, speaking in a soft tone, sometimes almost whispering to herself. When the puppets begin to live in the scene her voice changes, becoming more sung than spoken, the pitch of her spoken voice being taken over by her singing voice. Her recitative is not sing-song rhythmic, but the rhythm freely moves with the intention of the shepherd boy as he jumps from stone to stone. The pitch of the girl's voice is a colourful monotone: the pitch remains much the same, but the tone colour is enlivened through the intensity and quality of the words as the shepherd crosses the stream. There are moments when a word is spoken, then the narrative is sung again.

When the shepherd arrives at the castle gates, the princess calls down to him from her high tower. She is far away, and the girl reaches up with her voice to the distant place where the princess lives, and sings her greetings down to the shepherd. The girl's voice is high now, but the intervals she sings are not large, they are between a third and a fifth. The high pitch of her voice, although it is not loud, has attracted some of the five-year-olds: several come over to the rug and lie on their stomachs, watching the play unfold. The shepherd now tells the princess of his wish that she come down and go with him. The simple recitative changes to a declamatory aria: a melody of several different tones arises, moving stepwise, the girl's voice becomes more intense as the shepherd pleads his cause. There is little repetition in the melody, but the movement contained in it provides a musical mood which waits expectantly for the princess's reply . . .

In the meantime, the snowplough has already cleared quite a few streets. It has come back to make a second round to scatter the grit and salt . . . The four-year-olds slicing apples jump up from the table. The noise of all those chestnuts hitting a wooden floor is so wonderful, they want to join the fun! The "mothers" putting their children to bed are angry that the snowplough has woken up their little ones, now the babies are crying . . . Some of the children polishing stones and grating chestnuts try throwing their stones and chestnuts on the floor – what a good idea, it makes a lovely *cracking* sound . . .

. . . the five-year-olds listening to the play hold their breaths as the princess agrees to go with the shepherd but he must first ask permission from her father, the king . . . The princess's instructions are sung to him in a melody of seconds with a strong, definite rhythm . . .

An observer can hardly believe that the chestnut-strewn chaos in the other half of the room (which the teacher is quickly helping to put right again) does not seem to penetrate the sheath of peacefulness which surrounds the puppet play. The children gathered around it show no sign that anything else in the room has taken place . . .

At the successful conclusion of the play, the children watching it lie still. The girl covers the scene with a cloth and sings in a half-whispering tone a farewell to the story of the shepherd and the princess. As her voice fades, there is a moment of absolute silence. Then the five-year-olds run back to the polishing table and the girl goes to the teacher to ask how long it will be until snack.

This description of a six-year-old girl's singing contains many elements of what has come to be called "Mood of the Fifth" music: the singing follows the rhythm of speech; melodies are simple, moving within intervals of seconds and thirds – sometimes as large as a fifth, rarely larger; melodies are often sung on one tone, the pitch taken from the speaking voice; the melodies are not written in major or in minor keys and have an open-ended feel to them. Above all is the mood of the music: when sung properly it seems to reach out and enfold the children in a protective sheath which has a quality of stillness and peace, although the children themselves may be active within it.

This music is a musical expression of an experience which is striven for in all aspects of Waldorf Education. It is difficult to describe in words, perhaps: "I am centred in my activity," "My thinking, feeling and willing are in balance." One feels deeply united with a task, at peace and yet still active. The young child finds this mood in play. S/he is deeply engaged in an activity which is then no longer interesting when the activity is over. The moment of silence at the end of the play was not a moment of reflection, but a moment which allowed the activity of watching the play to come to a complete end before the next task could engage the children's attention.

The broader context of this musical experience should be noted: the kindergarten just described is one where mood-of-the-fifth music was not cultivated by the teacher. The children learned only traditional children's songs and games which were sung in strict rhythm, and with major or minor key melodies. The six-year-old girl experienced similar music at home.

Yet the girl's singing is not an isolated or unusual musical event. Such singing can often be heard when a child's attention is fully engaged in his/her play. We grown-ups tend to dismiss such fragments of melody as noise, or incomplete attempts by the child to sing our music, not listening closely enough to discover the innate coherence of the child's activity. Too often well-meaning adults try to "correct" the pitch which is too high, or the rhythm which is irregular, and slowly wall in a living musicality with "proper" songs . . . Sooner or later, often at puberty, an attempt is made at breaking through these walls, as the pounding beat of popular music has long suggested.

The use of "Mood of the Fifth" music in the kindergarten encompasses two considerations. It is first of all a path of musical development for the adult, which schools his/her musical perception and ability so that s/he is able to participate in a musicality which the children *already possess.* This musicality may, for many reasons, lie dormant or misshapen within an individual child or group of children. Through the adult's use of Mood of the Fifth s/he can reawaken and bring back into movement the musicality which is so essential for the full development of the child's soul life. (To be labelled "unmusical" or "tone deaf" causes deep, lingering wounds to the child's self esteem. There are unfortunately many adults who can attest to the truth of this statement out of their own experience.)

Mood of the Fifth music can also help the adult to establish an additional point of contact with the child which shows him/her that the adult *understands.* One of the rewards of working with young children is surely the open look of delight on a child's face when s/he hears a story, plays a game, experiences something which pleases him/her. The look of delight means more, however, than just "I like that." On a deeper level it expresses the child's trust in the adult: "You know who I am, and what you offer me is that which I am searching for with my deepest intentions. I can follow you."

The present day task of the Waldorf Kindergarten is primarily a therapeutic one. It provides children with basic experiences which they need for healthy development, overcoming deficiencies which often occur today in the first years of life. A very large part of these experiences are sensory, as the development of the physical senses (touch, balance, etc.) lays the foundation for the later unfolding of the spiritual capacities (thinking, speech, etc.). The kindergarten is not a mirror of our daily lives, but an extract of the many activities, distilled to their essence. This provides a simplicity and basic necessity for the content of kindergarten life which the child can understand and imitate wholeheartedly. The meaningful activity around the child awakens his/her interest in the world, and this interest becomes the mainspring of later learning.

In the arts the materials presented to the child are restricted to essentials, and with these the child's imagination has free rein. This can be clearly seen, for example, in painting: the three primary colours are used – red, yellow and blue. The children are given watercolours, a large wet sheet of paper and a broad brush to paint with. The materials themselves preclude any precise drawing, colours flow into one another, sometimes mixing, sometimes remaining pure side by side. There is no right or wrong way of using the colours, the expansive, fiery or cool moods of the colours themselves guide the child's brush. The medium of water enables the child's soul to breathe freely in the movement of colour with the brush. If only the paper were bigger s/he could paint on and on . . .

Music can be approached in a similar way. Here as well the materials can be restricted so that the *activity* becomes of foremost importance. Only five different tones of our twelve tone system are used:

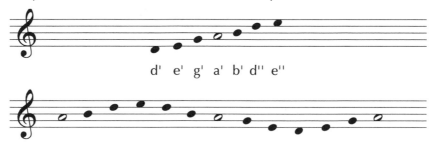

d' e' g' a' b' d'' e''

When a children's harp or lyre is used, the strings are tuned to pure fifths (like a violin's open strings) rather than the tempered intervals of the piano. The songs are not written in major or minor keys, but tend to circle around the middle tone, a'. The rhythm is free, either gently swinging (3 or 6 beats) or walking (2 or 4 beats), but the movement of the music takes its impulse from the words and seeks to accompany its inner content.

This style of music making lends itself wonderfully to the activities of circle time where movement, the spoken word and song freely flow from one to the other, just as the three basic colours do in painting. Teachers who have worked with Mood of the Fifth music in the classroom also know of its effectiveness in creating moments where the attention of all of the children is engaged, enabling a special mood to arise, whether in a puppet play, grace before meal, etc.

Newcomers to this music may at first experience difficulty in hearing the melodies or finding an inner connection to them. Others may have trouble finding the beginning pitch or singing the songs as high as they are written. None of these difficulties should be considered unsolvable problems.

Over time, the practice of Music of the Fifth songs often leads to a good sense of pitch. The voice gradually learns the placement of the tones, and the reduced number of tones make sight-singing possible even for the "unmusical" person.

Difficulty in reaching the higher notes (d", e"), which lie within traditional singing range of soprano and altos, can be due to breathing which is too shallow, as well as to the false idea that high notes are more difficult to sing and require greater effort. In the long run, the question of extending the vocal range is best addressed by an experienced teacher. But those without a teacher can still consider the following: the vocal range can be affected by physical movement. Often much can be accomplished by accompanying a song with large, simple, physical gestures. This helps free the breathing, allowing greater ease in reaching notes which are "too high." The songs can be practised with movement until the feeling of vocal mobility is secure. Then the outward movement can gradually become smaller and disappear altogether, all the while maintaining the inner freedom of movement in the voice.

An essential guide for adults who wish to find a path into the experience of Mood of the Fifth music can be found in Julius Knierim's *Songs in the Mood of the Fifth (Quintenlieder)*. This succinct and clearly written booklet describes, with simple exercises and musical examples, a path which really can be taken by all who have a sincere interest in further development of their musical abilities. By working with the suggestions contained in Julius Knierim's essay, the serious student can develop capacities which not only lead him/her into the musical world of the young child, but can help build a new relationship to traditional classical music, and to all further musical development.

Rudolf Steiner, in discussing music for the young child, spoke of the great importance of the Quintenstimmung = *Mood* of the Fifth. The suggestions mentioned in this article, and most especially in Dr. Knierim's book, are guideposts by which adults may find the way into this mood. They are not the mood itself. Individual observation, experimentation, and practice are the means by which the letter of the law may be enlivened by its spirit.

The goal of these booklets is to offer immediate practical help in working with young children. It is for this reason that a variety of musical styles is included. All songs (as well as stories and verses) have proved their worth in Waldorf kindergartens or other settings with young children. Some traditional tunes with new words have been included, and many traditional rhymes have been set to new melodies (either pentatonic or Mood of the Fifth). Familiar children's songs have been excluded for the most part because these are readily available in other collections. Most songs are set in D-pentatonic. This is done for pedagogical as well as practical reasons (see references). Experience has shown that many teachers and parents who wish to consciously address music-making with the young child are often just those who are themselves struggling with their own musical education. With most songs written in D-pentatonic mode (which are tones of a Choroi flute or children's harp, and are easy to play on a traditional recorder), it is hoped that the initial difficulties with note reading and transposition will be eased. The use of bar lines and time signatures varies, showing new possibilities of notation. Some songs have traditional time signatures, others have only a 3 or 4 at the beginning to indicate a more swinging or walking rhythm. The absence of bar lines leaves the singer free to determine the musical phrasing according to the rhythm of the words and their sense. Commas indicate a slight pause, or point of rest.

Jennifer Aulie

References:

Knierim, Julius. *Songs in the Mood of the Fifth 'Quintenlieder'.*
ISBN: 0 945803 14 1 (Rudolf Steiner College Press, California)

Steiner, Rudolf. *The Study of Man.*
ISBN: 0 85584 187 8 (Rudolf Steiner Press, England)

Steiner, Rudolf. *The Inner Nature of Music and the Experience of Tone.*
ISBN 0 88010 074 5 (Steiner Books, Massachusetts)

1. The snowflakes sink down,
   And 'neath their white gown
   There hides a white crown:
   Three wee flowers you see.

2. Their heads are bent low,
   Their hearts do not show
   Who dreams 'neath the snow?
   Three wee bells you see.

3. But soon they will ring
   And tell us of spring.
   Who can it be?
   Snowdrops are we.

1. Snowdrops, snowdrops, little drops of snow,
   What do you do when the cold winds blow?
   Hide our little heads and say,
   Cold winds, cold winds go away.

2. Snowdrops, snowdrops, dressed in green and white,
   What do you do when the sun shines bright?
   Shake our little bells and sing,
   Ting-a-ling, ting-a-ling, here's the spring.

E. Kudar   *E. Kudar*

Snow - drop, wake up: Spring is com - ing,

Spring is com - ing. Snow - drop, wake up:

Spring is com - ing, Spring is here.

THE COLTSFOOT

The winds of March are keen and cold,
I fear them not for I am bold.
I wait not for my leaves to grow,
They follow after, they are slow.
My yellow blooms are brave and bright,
I greet the spring with all my might.

When the snow is on the ground
Little bells are to be found:
Hush! Tread soft for I can see
Snowdrops sweet for you and me.

From Germany

18

1. When March wind blows, "Who-oo-oo-oo,"
   In a gruff and growly way,
   He's saying, "Keep your mittens on.
   I'm blowing cold today."

2. But when he blows, "Who-oo-oo-oo,"
   In a soft and gentle way,
   He's saying, "Take your snowsuit off,
   I'm blowing warm today."

   A. Richter

1. King Winter sat on his throne one day
   And he said to himself, said he:
   "I must admit I've had some fun,
   I've chilled the earth and cooled the sun,
   And not a flower or tree
   But wishes that my reign were done.
   As long as time and tide shall run
   I'll go on making everyone,
   As cold as cold can be."

2. There came a knock at the outer door
   "Who's there," King Winter cried.
   "Open your palace gates," said Spring,
   "For you reign no more as King.
   No longer here abide.
   This message from the sun I bring
   The trees are green, the birds do sing
   The hills with joy are echoing.
   So pray, Sir, step outside."

   H. Chesterman

M. Meyerkort   N. Foster

In the spring-time gar - den,
ro - sy morn - ing glow,
Sun - shine call - ing, fall - ing, call - ing,
seed - lings wake and grow.

Down in the earth in their dark winter bed
Someone is calling, the crocus said.
In colours bright they quickly dressed,
In lavender, purple and gold of the best.
Then out in the grass they dance in a ring
And call to the children, "Come out! It is spring."

H. Henley

P. Patterson

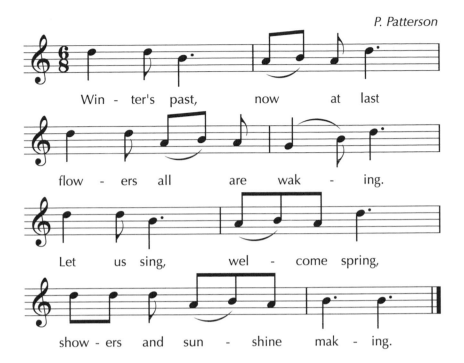

Win - ter's past, now at last
flow - ers all are wak - ing.
Let us sing, wel - come spring,
show - ers and sun - shine mak - ing.

2. No more snow, flowers grow,
   Show their lovely faces,
   Colours bright, red and white,
   Filling empty spaces.

Crocus, crocus waken up
And catch a sunbeam in your cup.

M. Meyerkort

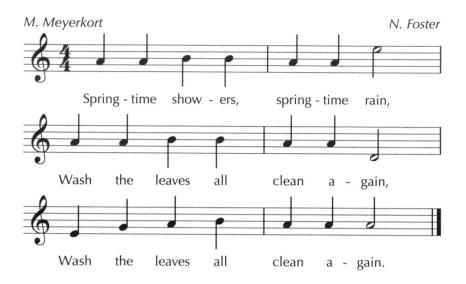

M. Meyerkort

N. Foster

Spring - time show - ers, spring - time rain,

Wash the leaves all clean a - gain,

Wash the leaves all clean a - gain.

1. In the heart of a seed,
   Buried deep so deep,
   A dear little plant
   Lay fast asleep.

2. Wake, said the sun,
   And creep to the light.
   Wake, said the voice
   Of the raindrops bright.

3. The little plant heard,
   And arose to see
   What the wonderful
   Outside world might be.

K. Brown

The sil - ver rain - drops pat - ter up -
Tip, tap, their knock is gen - tle and

on the earth to - day. Oh
this is what they say: Come

lit - tle flowers a - wak - en and
out in pret - ty dress - es for

o - pen wide your door.
spring is here once more.

N. de Bruyne   N. de Bruyne

Rain   flow, wind blow, sun glow,

Help   the earth the seed to grow.

Traditional

N. Foster

My La - dy Spring is dressed in green, she
And lit - tle ba - by buds and twigs are

wears a prim - rose crown, The
cling - ing to her gown;

sun shines if she laughs___ at all, and

if she weeps the rain - drops fall. My

La - dy Spring, my La - dy Spring, my

La - dy Spring. ___

A little brown bulb went to sleep in the ground.
In his little brown nightie he slept very sound.
Old Winter he roared and he raged overhead,
But the little brown bulb did not move in his bed.

But when Spring came tiptoeing over the lea
With fingers to lips as soft as can be.
The little brown bulb just lifted his head,
Slipped off his nightie and jumped out of bed.

A. Fairman

A little garden flower
Is lying in its bed.
A warm spring sun
Is shining overhead.
Down came the raindrops
Dancing to and fro –
The little flower wakens
And then begins to grow.

High on the hilltop I fly my new kite;
Springtime is kite-time and full of delight;
Kite on the wing, I hold the string;
Pull away, tug away, kite in the sky.

A. Carpenter

J. Mehta

J. Mehta

Wake up, wake up, all you lit - tle child - ren. Sun - light sky bright, spring is com - ing now. Gust - y March winds blow - ing, daf - fo - dils a - blow - ing. Birds sing, bells ring, there's blos-som on the bough.

2. Piper, piper, play your happy music.
    Singing, singing, we will follow on.
    Dancing through the daytime, lead us to the May-time.
    Sing dong, spring song – the winter's past and gone.

A little seedling went to rest
For winter's deep and long repose.
Thousands of stars did all their best
To weave a mantle for his clothes,
And dreaming in his sleep he stands
In beautiful, green fairylands.
And then with merry laugh and shout
A host of gnomes comes leaping out.
They chuckle, giggle, start to tear
The little seedling by his hair.
Through clouds a cheeky sunbeam peeps,
He laughs as loudly as he can:
I'll pull his hair, you pull his legs –
And here awakes the little man.
Out of his dream arising, see,
A great big giant of a tree.

Little by little, the acorn said,
As it slowly sank in its mossy bed,
I am improving every day,
Hidden deep in the earth away.
Little by little, each day it grew,
Little by little it sipped the dew,
Downward it sent out a tiny root,
Up in the air sprang a tiny shoot.
Day after day and year after year,
Little by little the leaves appear.
The slender branches spread far and wide,
Till the mighty oak is the forest's pride.

J. Mehta   J. Mehta

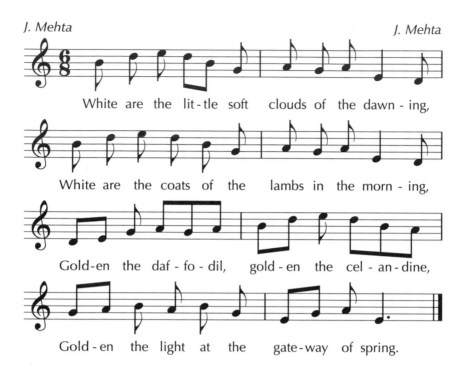

White are the lit-tle soft clouds of the dawn-ing,

White are the coats of the lambs in the morn-ing,

Gold-en the daf-fo-dil, gold-en the cel-an-dine,

Gold-en the light at the gate-way of spring.

2. Blue are the shy little violets hiding,
   Blue the great sky where the skylarks go gliding.
   Come let us sing now, all in a ring now,
   Joyful our song as we welcome the spring.

   Golden sun in heaven blue
   Come and warm us through and through.
   Come and give us of your gold
   That the blossom may unfold.

P. Patterson

I know a lit - tle puss - y, her
She lives down in the mea - dow not

coat is pear - ly grey, She'll
ve - ry far a - way. For

al - ways be a pus - sy she'll
she's a pus - sy wil - low, now

ne - ver ___ be a cat,
what do you think of that?

Miaow, miaow, miaow, miaow, miaow, miaow, miaow.

Hark, the ti - ny cow - slip bell
Birds in ev' - ry wood - land dell

In the breeze is ring - ing,
Songs of joy are sing - ing:

"Win - ter's o'er, spring once more

Spreads a - broad her gold - en store."

Hark, the ti - ny cow - slip bell

In the breeze is ring - ing.

2. "Spring has come to make us glad   Hearts are gay, blithe as May,
    Let us give her greeting."   Dance and sing the livelong day:
    Winter days were cold and sad,   "Spring has come to make us glad
    Winter's reign is fleeting.   Let us give her greeting."

1. Sweet and low the south wind blows,
   Across the field he calling goes:
   Come pussy, pussy willow.

2. Within your close brown wrapper stir,
   Come out and show your silver fur,
   Come pussy, pussy willow.

Baby seedlings wrapped up tight
In their cosy nest of night.
Gently, gently will they wake
With a little springtime shake.

Lady Spring, Lady Spring, widely loving everything.

The gnomes will tug each little root,
And green will grow each little shoot,
And as their lovely leaves unfold,
They put on flower caps of gold.

Lady Spring, Lady Spring, widely loving everything.

O, Spring it is a shining shower,
Of bud and shoot and leaf and flower,
Unfolding daily one by one
Their rainbow treasures to the sun.

W. Gerst and J. Mehta

March winds and April show'rs
Bring forth May flow'rs.

Daffodil, it's such a lovely day,
Won't you open wide your buds? Hark, the sunbeams say.
Little daffodilly put on your yellow gown.
"Look, am I not handsome, in my golden crown?"

I. Thompson   *H. Koteen*

I have heard a mo-ther bird   Sing-ing in the rain,

Tell-ing all her lit-tle ones,   Spring has come a - gain.

2. I have seen a wave of green,
    Down a lovely lane,
    Making all the hedges glad:
    Spring has come again.

3. I have found a patch of ground,
    Golden in the sun,
    Crocuses are calling out:
    Spring has come again!

Come with me,
Oh, come and see!
There are blossoms now
On the beechnut tree,
And though the oak tree
Is dark and bare,
A pair of robins
Are nesting there:
And any minute
The willows lean
Will burst out in leaf –
Their tips are green,
So come along,
Oh, come with me –
It's spring again,
And there's lots to see.

P. Patterson *P. Patterson*

Black - bird, black - bird on the high tree,

Black - bird, black - bird fly down to me!

Traditional

N. Foster

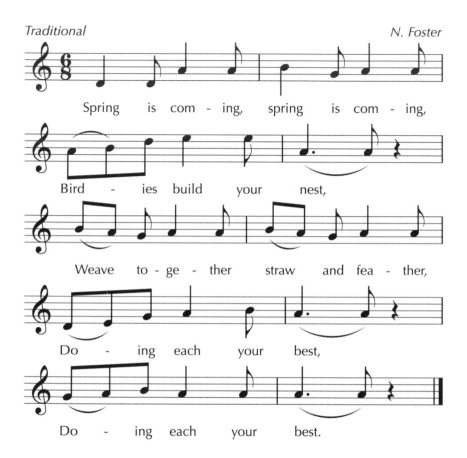

Spring is com - ing, spring is com - ing,

Bird - ies build your nest,

Weave to - ge - ther straw and fea - ther,

Do - ing each your best,

Do - ing each your best.

2. Spring is coming, spring is coming,
   Flowers are waking too,
   Daisies, lilies, daffodilies,
   Now are coming through.

3. Spring is coming, spring is coming,
   All around is fair,
   Shimmer, glimmer on the meadow,
   Joy is everywhere.

A. Matthews

Come, oh come, ye lit - tle gnomes,

Let us leave our moun - tain homes,

We'll free the Flow - er Queen And

make her a throne in the mea - dow green.

2. Take your hammer, take your sack,
   Lift and take it on your back,
   We'll free the Flower Queen
   And make her a throne in the meadow green.

Here we build in meadow green,
A shining throne for the Flower Queen.

1. Busy gnomes
    Bring to birth
    Little seeds
    In the earth.

2. Water spirits
    Feed the shoots
    Striving upwards
    From the roots.

3. Airy sylphs
    Power bestow
    Make the plant
    Thrive and grow.

4. Sun sprites bring
    Warming gold
    Many hued
    Buds in fold.

5. Flowers all
    Secrets keep
    In their hearts
    New seeds sleep.

6. Water, fire,
    Earth and air
    In this work
    Have a share
    That the earth
    Seeds may bear.

I thank you gnomes for your sheltering hand,
From the winter cold and drear,
In the soft, brown earth I lived warm and safe,
The cold I need not fear.
But now in the golden rays of the sun
I mount my throne again,
And scatter the fields and woods with flowers,
Bringing joy to the hearts of men.

1. With glee, with glee, we goblin gnomes
   Are leaving moss and mountain homes.
   With little hammers bright
   We work with all our might
   To free the Flower Queen.

2. From deepest earth to light and air
   We make a way for the lady fair.
   With little hammers bright
   We work with all our might
   To free the Flower Queen.

3. Our hammers work ding dong, ding dong,
   We dig and dig with axes strong.
   The hard earth breaks away
   And happily this day
   We greet the Flower Queen.

1. Buttercups and daisies
   Oh, the pretty flowers,
   Coming ere the springtime
   To tell of sunny hours,
   While the trees are leafless,
   While the fields are bare,
   Buttercups and daisies
   Spring up here and there.

2. Ere the snowdrop peepeth,
   Ere the crocus bold,
   Ere the early primrose
   Opes its paly gold,
   Somewhere on the sunny bank
   Buttercups are bright.
   Somewhere 'mong the frozen grass
   Peeps the daisy white.

M. Howitt

In many lands the children bring
May Baskets for the first of spring,
And hang them on a neighbour's door
To say that spring is here once more.

A. Wynne

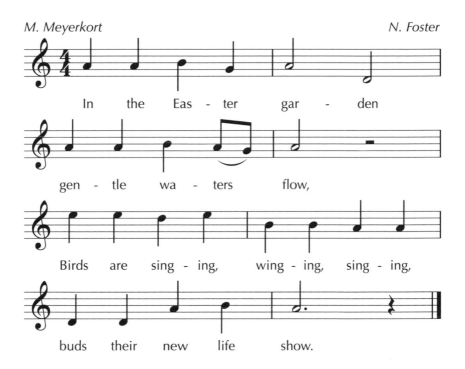

M. Bucknall

M. Bucknall

From the hills flow the stream - lets and
laugh - ing they say: now Eas - ter is com - ing and
spring's on the way. *Verse 1:* The
rain and the wind and the sun and the earth sing:
Eas - ter is com - ing and spring - time is here.

2. Hear the birdies are calling
   And laughing they say:
   Now Easter is coming and spring's on the way.

3. See the green shoots are sprouting
   And laughing they say:
   Now Easter is coming and spring's on the way.

4. Hark, the flower bells are ringing
   And laughing they say:
   Now Easter is coming and spring's on the way.

Continued...

5. The rain and the wind,
   And the sun and the earth
   Sing Easter is coming and springtime is here.

6. All creatures rejoice
   And the people on earth
   Sing Easter is coming and springtime is here.

N. Foster   N. Foster

Cat - er - pil - lar creep a - bout,

Round and round and in and out.

When you are fed come spin your bed,

Go to sleep, deep, deep,

As a cat - er - pil - lar die,

Wak - en as a but - ter - fly.

A caterpillar crawled to the top of a tree.
"I think I'll take a nap," said he.
So – under a leaf he began to creep
To spin his cocoon, and he fell asleep.
All winter he slept in his cocoon bed,
Till spring came along one day and said,
"Wake up, wake, up, little sleepyhead.
Wake up, it's time to get out of bed."
So – he opened his eyes that sunshiny day.
Lo! He was a butterfly – and flew away!

1. Fuzzy, wuzzy, creepy, crawly,
    Caterpillar, fat and funny.
    You will be a butterfly,
    When the days are soft and sunny.

2. Winging, winging, flying, singing,
    Butterfly so bright and yellow
    You were once a caterpillar,
    Wriggly, wiggly, wormly fellow.

1. See the little butterfly
    How he gaily flutters by,
    Settles on a buttercup,
    Then once more goes flying up.

2. Welcome, little butterfly
    We will love you as you fly,
    On your journey safely come
    With a message from the sun.

Traditional

N. Foster

Wa - ken, sleep - ing but - ter - fly

Burst your nar - row pris - on.

Spread your gold - en wings and fly,

For the sun has ris - en.

Spread your wings and tell the sto - ry,

How He rose, the King of Glo - ry.

THE LAMB

I have a coat
A lovely coat
As white as milk
As soft as silk
And as warm as a quilt.
I am
A happy little lamb.

I. Tupaj

Too-ee!   Too-ee!   Too-ee!
A little bird sings in the hawthorn tree:
I sing and I sing for a bright-eyed wife,
To share in my thorny and blossomy life.
We'll build us a nest in the hawthorn tree
With little blue eggs in it, one, two, three.
Then mother shall sit and shall keep them warm
And I'll go a-digging a fine fat worm.
Too-ee!   Too-ee! Too-ee!
What happy birds we'll be!
With little babies three,
With spring, white spring
In the hawthorn tree.
Too-ee!   Too-ee!   Too-ee!

Easter Hare! His ears are floppy.
Easter Hare! His feet are hoppy.
His fur is soft,
And nose is fluffy,
Tail is short and powder-puffy.

THE HARE

From Germany   *J. Aulie*

See, the lit-tle hare so fast a - sleep,
fast a - sleep. Lit - tle hare, O
are you ill, that you lie so
qui - et and still? Hop lit - tle hare,
hop lit - tle hare, hop an - y where.

Suggested directions:

Toddlers: **First 4 lines:** *children crouch on the floor.*
                       Last line: *children hop about.*

Nursery children: **First 4 lines:** *some children walk in open circle*
                       formation, while others crouch in the centre.
                       Last line: *children in the centre hop to a chosen*
                       child in the circle, and touch his/her feet. These
                       children now become the new hares.

Ann Elliott

J. Aulie

I have made a pret - ty nest,

Look in - side, look in - side,

Hun - gry bir - dies with their beaks,

O - pen wide, o - pen wide,

See my lit - tle bir - dies grow,

Day by day, day by day,

Till they spread their lit - tle wings and

then they fly a - way.

1. When a little chicken eats,
    He scampers all around.
    Picking here and picking there,
    Bits of dinner from the ground.

2. When a little chicken drinks,
    He stands so very still,
    While the water trickles down
    Through his upturned bill.

1. Awake, awake, it's springtime,
    The gentle breezes blow,
    The sunshine whispers to the flow'rs,
    "Awake, awake, and grow!"

2. So raise our happy voices
    As bells of Easter ring,
    And say with sunshine, birds and flow'rs,
    "Awake, awake, it's spring!"

M. W. Clark

Easter bells are ringing,
Hear the cheerful sound;
Easter flow'rs are springing,
See them all around;
Happy voices singing
Joyful roundelay:
"Peace and love we're bringing,
Blessed Easter Day!"

1. All the birds have come again,
   All the birds together.
   Hark the warbling, whistling, singing,
   Every bird his music bringing,
   All the world with song is ringing.
   Welcome to the springtime.

2. What a joyful merry throng
   Darting through the branches.
   Blackbird, starling, finch and thrush,
   Chirp and perch in every bush.
   O'er the meadows in a rush
   Spring comes gaily dancing.

3. News has come from far and near –
   Hearken to the voices.
   Listen how the meadows ring.
   Children gaily dance and sing.
   All the world doth greet the spring,
   Every heart rejoices.

From Germany

"Come, little children,"
Calls mother hen.
"It is time to take
Your nap again."
And under feathers
The small ducks creep,
And she clucks a song
Till they fall asleep.

N. Foster

Lit - tle snail, lit - tle snail,

On the rock you leave a trail,

Car - ry your house up - on your back, It

takes so long to get there and back, But

e - ven though you're not ve - ry fast, You're

hap - py the spring sun has come at last.

Prickly ball, unroll yourself –
Show your sniffly snout,
Show your shining little eyes,
Patter all about;
Prickly ball unrolls himself –
Comes a hedgehog out!

M. de Havas   J. Kellman

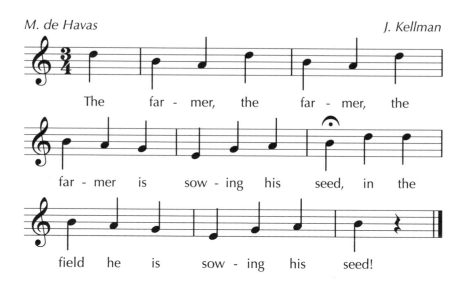

The far - mer, the far - mer, the

far - mer is sow - ing his seed, in the

field he is sow - ing his seed!

I dig, dig, dig,
And I plant some seeds.
I rake, rake, rake,
And I pull some weeds.
I wait and watch
And soon I know,
My garden sprouts
And starts to grow.

Dig! Dig! Dig! Rake just so.
Plant the seeds, watch them grow.
Chop! Chop! Chop! Pull out weeds.
Warm rain and sun, my garden needs.
Up! Up! Up! Green stems climb.
Open wide, it's blossom time!

Dig a little hole.
Plant a little seed.
Pour a little water.
Pull a little weed.

Chase a little bug –
Heigh-ho, there he goes!
Give a little sunshine.
Grow a little rose.

A farmer once planted some little brown seeds
With a pit-a-pit, pit-a-pit, pit-a-pit, pat.
He watered them often and pulled out the weeds
With a tug-tug at this and a tug-tug at that.
The seeds they grew tall and grew green in the sun
With a push-push up here and a push-push up there,
And a beautiful plant grew from every one
With a hey diddle holding their heads in the air.

I. Westrup

1. Please show me how to turn the earth,
    Turn the earth, turn the earth,
    Please show me how to turn the earth
    That I may make a garden!

    > *Oh, lovely garden, well begun,*
    > *Drink in the rain, enjoy the sun!*
    > *And should you bloom or should you not.*
    > *You are my own dear garden spot.*

2. Oh! This is the way to turn the earth,
    Turn the earth, turn the earth,
    Oh! This is the way to turn the earth
    If you would make a garden.

    Chorus

3. Please show me how to plant the seed,
    Plant the seed, plant the seed,
    Please show me how to plant the seed
    That I may make a garden!

    Chorus

4. Oh! This is the way to plant the seed,
    Plant the seed, plant the seed,
    Oh! This is the way to plant the seed
    If you would make a garden.

    Chorus

5. Please show me how the sprinkler goes,
    Sprinkler goes, sprinkler goes,
    Please show me how the sprinkler goes
    That I may make a garden!

    Chorus

Continued...

6. Oh! This is the way the sprinkler goes,
   Sprinkler goes, sprinkler goes,
   Oh! This is the way the sprinkler goes
   If you would make a garden.

   Chorus.

   A. Riley

E. Hutchins   *E. Lebret*

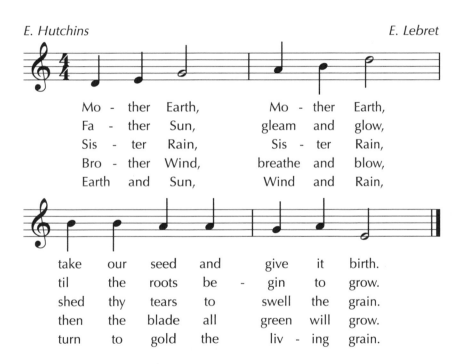

Mo - ther	Earth,	Mo - ther	Earth,
Fa - ther	Sun,	gleam and	glow,
Sis - ter	Rain,	Sis - ter	Rain,
Bro - ther	Wind,	breathe and	blow,
Earth and	Sun,	Wind and	Rain,

take	our	seed	and	give	it	birth.
til	the	roots	be -	gin	to	grow.
shed	thy	tears	to	swell	the	grain.
then	the	blade	all	green	will	grow.
turn	to	gold	the	liv - ing	grain.

There lies a lonely field,
The soil is brown and bare.
And so the farmer comes along
And fences it in with care.

And then he brings his plough,
And ploughs from morn till late.
Across the field and back again
He ploughs the furrows straight.

Now pull the harrow well
To make the soil more loose.
The harrow combs the soil so soft
And makes it fit for use.

Then Johnny brings the corn
To sow the seed just so.
And in and out they swing their arm
As up and down they go.

1. Your rake and shovel and wheelbarrow bring;
   Let's plant us a garden this morning in spring;
   Dig little trenches, pull out all the weeds;
   Pour in some water, then drop in your seeds.

2. Be sure you cover them all 'ere you go;
   Now rake the top over and leave them to grow.
   Shine, merry sunlight, and fall, gentle rain!
   Tend to my garden till I come again.

R. Compton

With horse and plough
To work we go
In furrow brown
The corn to sow.
To springing plants
The sun gives birth,
While roots are held
In clasp of earth.
With wind and rain,
With warmth and light,
The force of heart
And hand unite,
That corn may grow
The meal to give,
To make the bread
Whereby we live.

From Germany

1. The farmer on the lowland
   Ever paces to and fro,
   Sowing barley in the springtime,
   Ever hoping it will grow;
   Sowing barley as he paces,
   In the springtime of the year;
   When the fruit trees are in blossom,
   Sowing barley far and near.

2. The farmer on the lowland
   Ever paces to and fro,
   Reaping barley in the autumn,
   Leaving stacks all in a row;
   Reaping barley as he paces,
   In the autumn of the year;
   When the grain is ripe and golden,
   Reaping barley far and near.

THE FARMER'S IN HIS DEN

Traditional   *J. Aulie*

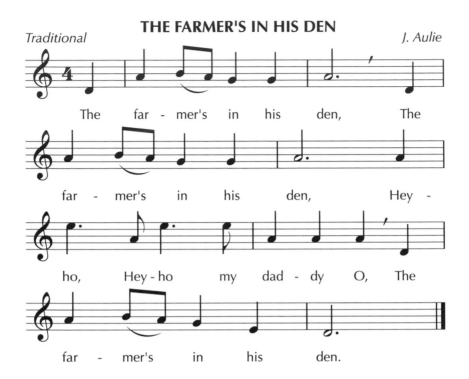

The far - mer's in his den, The

far - mer's in his den, Hey -

ho, Hey - ho my dad - dy O, The

far - mer's in his den.

2. The farmer takes a wife,
   The farmer takes a wife,
   Hey-ho my daddy O,
   The farmer takes a wife.

3. The wife takes a child,
   The wife takes a child,
   Hey-ho my daddy O,
   The wife takes a child.

4. The child takes a nurse,
   The child takes a nurse,
   Hey-ho my daddy O,
   The child takes a nurse.

Continued...

5. The nurse takes a dog,
   The nurse takes a dog,
   Hey-ho my daddy O,
   The nurse takes a dog.

6. The dog takes a bone,
   The dog takes a bone,
   Hey-ho my daddy O,
   The dog takes a bone.

7. We all pat the bone,
   We all pat the bone,
   Hey-ho my daddy O,
   We all pat the bone.

Suggested directions:

Children walk in open circle formation. One child stands in the centre representing the farmer, maybe for the first few verses with an adult.
At the end of verse 2 the farmer chooses another child as the 'wife' to come to the centre, and so on.

Traditional   M. Bucknall

Now here we go round ___ the
May - pole high, The May - pole high, the
May - pole high, Now here we go round the
May - pole high, Let col - oured rib - bons
fly, ___ Let col - oured rib - bons fly. ___

2. See lasses and lads go tripping by,
    Go tripping by, go tripping by,
    See lasses and lads go tripping by,
    Let coloured ribbons fly.
    Let coloured ribbons fly.

3. In rainbow hues make garlands gay,
    Make garlands gay, make garlands gay,
    In rainbow hues make garlands gay,
    Let coloured ribbons fly,
    Let coloured ribbons fly.

58

From Holland   *J. Aulie*

Here's a branch of snow-y May, A
branch the fair - ies gave me.
Who would like to dance to-day, With a
branch the fair - ies gave me?
Dance a - way, dance a - way,
Hold - ing high the branch of May.

Verses 2 and 3: M. Bucknall

Suggested directions:

Children form a circle and walk around while 2 to 6 stand in the centre wearing a paper May-crown and holding a branch of either May or Queen Anne's Lace in their hands. They take a partner and change while the circle stands still. The partners are now May Queens and May Kings.

M. Meyerkort   J. Aulie

Nix in the wa - ter, You
are the Ri - ver King's daugh - ter.
Wash your legs with sil - ver sand and
tie your hair with a gold - en band.
Nix catch me! Nix catch me!

Suggested directions:

Some children form a circle and walk around while others crouch in the centre. At 'Wash your legs' the circle stands still and all rub thighs, then act as if tying a ribbon round their heads. Then 'Nixes' get up and put their arms around a child of their choice. These children will then be the new Nixes.

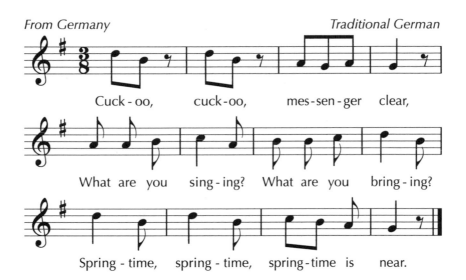

Cuck - oo,   cuck - oo,   mes - sen - ger   clear,

What are you   sing - ing?   What are you   bring - ing?

Spring - time,   spring - time,   spring - time is   near.

2. Cuckoo, cuckoo, sounding so clear,
   Winter is over,
   Pink grows the clover.
   Springtime, springtime, springtime is near.

3. Cuckoo, cuckoo, sing through the land.
   Gladly we hear you
   Now we are near you.
   Listen, listen, spring is at hand.

Good morning, lords and ladies,
It is the first of May,
We hope you'll like our singing,
It is so sweet and gay.
The cuckoo sings in April,
The cuckoo sings in May,
The cuckoo sings in June,
In July she flies away.
The cuckoo drinks cold water
To make her song so clear,
And then she sings "Cuckoo, Cuckoo,"
For three months of the year.

1. The cuckoo and the donkey
   They quarrelled one fine day,
   As to who could better sing
   In the lovely month of May.

2. The cuckoo said, now hear me,
   And so began to call.
   But I can do it better,
   And the donkey sang hee-haw.

3. This sweet and lovely music
   It echoed wide and far,
   They sang so well together,
   Cuckoo, cuckoo, hee-haw.

From Germany

From Germany
Traditional German

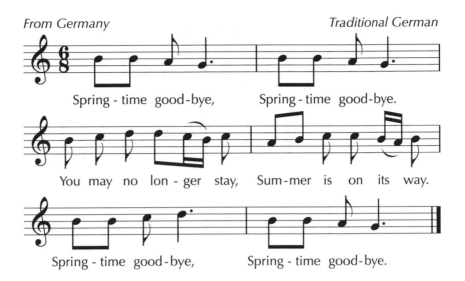

Spring - time good - bye, Spring - time good - bye.

You may no lon - ger stay, Sum - mer is on its way.

Spring - time good - bye, Spring - time good - bye.

Seeds

Once upon a time there was a little boy. He lived in a house surrounded by a garden. The trees and flowers were his friends.

One day Mother gave him a handful of seeds and said: "Let us go into the garden and plant these seeds in the earth. If we look after them we shall see how they will grow, with the help of their friends. The first helpers will be the rain fairies who will sing: 'It's time for you to wake up'. Then the earth fairies will come and they will help the roots to grow and to hold firm within the earth. The next helpers will be the wind fairies. They will play with the leaves and help the plants to stretch towards the sun. Then one day the plants will feel something shining and glowing on their buds. They will open their petals and whom will they see? The sun."

The child took the seeds into the garden and planted them in the earth. He tended and cared for them and together the child and the plants grew straight and strong.

E. Tuck

The Hare

In the time when the Jesus Child lived among men, the earth was beginning to die; the stout oaks could no longer withstand the storm; the delicate aspens shook as with an ague, and the flowers opened their blossoms only to gaze at the sun and wither away. Men and women wandered over the earth with sad hearts and listless eyes.

Only the Jesus Child knew that the earth would not die for he had come to bring life and hope. So he called the animals to him and said: "Which of you will be my messenger and journey through the world saying to everyone you meet, 'The earth will live anew, for the Jesus Child has come.'"

Then all the animals pressed around him saying, "Send me, send me." The Jesus Child saw that it would be difficult to choose, so he said, "The one who can most quickly circle the earth and return shall be my chosen messenger."

Then the wild stag thought, "I am the fleetest of foot – I shall win the race." And he went bounding over the hills. But when he came to the rocky highlands, he could not resist leaping over crag and burn and so happy was he in his game that he forgot the passing of the hours.

The salmon said to himself, "I can dart through the water, and float with the tide – I shall far outstrip the heavy-footed beasts." But when he saw the sunbeams sparkling on the stream, he thought they were golden flies. All day long he leapt, hoping to catch the bright winged vagrants. And so the day turned to its close.

The hawk exulted, "I am the swiftest of all who circle the earth." And he shot like an arrow through the blue. But suddenly his keen eye saw a tiny field mouse creeping among the corn. Straight as a plummet, he swooped – his journey was forgotten in the joy of the chase.

Only the hare kept quietly on his way. Turning neither to right nor left, gazing ever before him, he steadfastly held his course, and just as the sun was setting, he completed the circle of the earth. Thus it was that the hare became the messenger of the Jesus Child.

But when our Lord told him to bear the good tidings to all mankind, the hare was overcome with fear. "How shall I make them believe me?" Then the Jesus Child asked the raven for the gift of one of his eggs. "Show them this egg," said our Lord, "and say, 'just as the golden yolk shines in the egg, so the Child who has come from heaven has brought the light of the sun to earth and the earth will not die but live anew.'" Then the hare set forth upon his way with joy.

Fleet Foot

One warm spring morning, a hare came hopping through the green grass in the woods. He was full of happiness. "Good morning, Starling. Greetings, Golden Daffodils. Hello there, Prickly Hedgehog."

Then he met another hare. It was his friend Wagtail. "Hello, old friend," said Fleet Foot. But there was no time to talk. Wagtail had hurt his paw and a hound was chasing after him. Fleet Foot could hear the hound coming nearer through the leaves.

"Come quickly, Wagtail, and crouch down under this bush," said Fleet Foot. He helped his friend to hide. Then away he bounded through the trees and the dog followed after. Round and round he led the dog, over streams, through the fields, across the meadows.

At last Fleet Foot was tired out and wanted to rest. Then Father Sun looked down and saw the dog chasing the hare. "I will help Fleet Foot," he said. And he peeped out from behind a cloud and shone so brightly that the dog was dazzled and had to sit down. Quickly Fleet Foot slipped under the garden fence into the long grass and away. Now the hound had lost the scent of the hare, so he trotted home to the farm.

Next day Fleet Foot met Wagtail. "Happy springtime, Wagtail," he said. "Happy Easter, Fleet Foot," said Wagtail.

S. Baines

The Little Rooster and the Little Hen

Once upon a time, Little Rooster and Little Hen went out in the woods to hunt for strawberries, and they agreed to divide with each other all the fruit they found. First, Little Hen found a strawberry. "Cluck, cluck, cluck," she called and, when Little Rooster came, she shared the berry with him.

By and by Little Rooster, in his turn, found a strawberry; but he didn't call cluck, cluck. He gobbled the berry whole to get it all for himself, and the berry was so big, it stuck fast in his throat. Try as he would, he could not swallow it! He stretched out his neck, he shook his head, he jumped around on his two little legs, and then befell flat on the ground choking and choking and choking.

Little Hen came running to see how she could help him. Water was what he needed. So Little Hen ran to the brook, and she called, "Oh Brook, good Brook, please give me a drop of water, for my little partner, Rooster. He is lying flat on his back and choking and choking and choking.

But the brook said, "I will give you a drop of water when you bring me a leaf from the linden tree."

So Little Hen ran to the linden tree and called, "Oh Linden Tree, good Linden Tree, please give me one of your leaves that I may give it to the brook, that the brook may give me some water for my little partner, Rooster, who is lying flat on his back and choking and choking and choking."

But the linden tree said, "I will give you a leaf when you bring me a kerchief that the peasant woman is making."

So Little Hen ran off to the peasant woman and she called, "Oh Woman, good Woman, please give me a kerchief that I may give it to the linden tree, that the linden tree may give me a leaf, that I may give it to the brook, that the brook may give me some water for my little partner, Rooster, who is lying flat on his back and choking and choking and choking."

But the peasant woman said, "I will give you a kerchief when you bring me some silk from the Queen of Saba." So Little Hen ran to the Queen and called, "Oh Queen, please give me a bit of silk that I may give it to the woman, that she may give me a kerchief, that I may give it to the linden tree, that the linden tree may give me a leaf, that I may give it to the brook, that the brook may give me some water for my little partner, Rooster, who is lying flat on his back and choking and choking and choking."

But the Queen of Saba said, "I'll give you a piece of silk when you bring me a pair of shoes from the shoemaker." So Little Hen ran to the shoemaker and called, "Oh Shoemaker, please give me a pair of shoes, that I may give them to the Queen, that she may give me a piece of silk, that I may give it to the woman, that she may give me a kerchief, that I may give it to the linden tree, that the linden tree may give me a leaf, that I may give it to the brook, that the brook may give me some water for my little partner, Rooster, who is lying flat on his back and choking and choking and choking."

But the shoemaker said, "I'll give you a pair of shoes when you bring me some cream from the farmer's wife." So Little Hen flew to the farmer's wife and called, "Oh Farmer's Wife, please give me some cream, that I may give it to the shoemaker, that he may give me a pair of shoes, that I may give them to the Queen, that she may give me a piece of silk, that I may give it to the woman, that she may give me a kerchief, that I may give it to the linden tree, that the linden tree may give me a leaf, that I may give it to the brook, that the brook may give me some water for my little partner, Rooster, who is lying flat on his back and choking and choking and choking."

But the farmer's wife said, "I will give you some cream when you bring me a bag full of grass."

Well, Little Hen was all tired out. But still she ran off to the meadow and began to pluck the grass. She filled a whole bag full. Then she dragged the bag of grass away to the farmer's wife, and the farmer's wife gave her the cream.

So Little Hen gave the cream to the shoemaker who gave her a pair of shoes. And she took the shoes to the Queen of Saba who gave her a bit of silk. And she took the bit of silk to the peasant woman who gave her a kerchief. And she took the kerchief to the linden tree who gave her a leaf. And she took the leaf to the brook. And then and there, the brook gave her that drop of water!

Little Hen hurried back to the place where she had left Little Rooster. He was choking so at that moment he could hardly get his breath. But the Little Hen dropped the water into his beak and the water ran down his throat and washed that big strawberry down. Then Little Rooster jumped up and flapped his wings for joy.

"Cock-a-doodle-doo!" he cried. But after that, when Little Rooster found something good to eat, he shared it with Little Hen.

From the Czech Republic

The Rabbit and the Carrot

Fields and hills were covered with deep snow, and Rabbit had nothing to eat. She went out to search for food and found two carrots. Rabbit ate one carrot and then thought to herself, "It is snowing so much and is bitterly cold, surely Donkey has nothing to eat. I shall bring this carrot to him."

Rabbit went right away to Donkey's home. But Donkey was not there. Rabbit left the carrot there and hopped back home. Donkey had also gone out to look for food. He found a couple of potatoes and went back home satisfied. When he opened the door, he saw the carrot. "From where could this carrot have come?" Donkey wondered. Then he ate his potatoes and thought, "It is snowing so much and is so bitterly cold, surely Lamb has nothing to eat. I shall bring this carrot to her."

He brought the carrot to Lamb's home, but Lamb was not there. Carefully he laid the carrot inside and went back home. Lamb had also gone out to search for food. She found a head of cabbage and went back home satisfied. When she opened the door, she saw the carrot. "From where could this carrot have come?" Lamb wondered. Then she ate the head of cabbage and thought, "It is snowing so much and is so bitterly cold, surely Deer has nothing to eat. I shall bring this carrot to him."

Lamb took the carrot and carried it to Deer's home, but he was not there. Lamb laid the carrot down and ran quickly back home. Deer had also gone out to search for food. He found some green leaves and went back home satisfied. When he opened the door, he saw the carrot. "From where could this carrot have come?" Deer wondered. Then he ate the green leaves and thought, "It is snowing so much and is so bitterly cold, surely Rabbit has nothing to eat. I shall give this beautiful carrot to her."

And Deer ran quickly to Rabbit's house. But Rabbit had eaten until she was full, had gone to bed and was asleep. Deer did not wish to awaken her, so he very quietly laid the carrot inside the door.

When Rabbit awoke, she rubbed her eyes in wonder. The carrot was back again! She thought it over for a moment, then said, "Surely a good friend has brought this carrot to me!" Then she ate the carrot all up and it tasted very good!

From China

71

The Pearl Grey Cockerel

Once there was a cockerel which travelled round the world. On his way he found a letter. He picked it up with his beak and read:

> "Pearl Grey Cockerel, Pearl Grey Hen,
> Dilly Duck and Gaggly Goose,
> Goldfinch from the treetop,
> Come to Chick-Chick's wedding."

The cockerel went on and after a few steps he met the hen. "Where are you going, friend Cockerel?" – "I'm going to Chick-Chick's wedding." – "May I come too?" – "If you are invited, you may." He looked at the letter and read:

> "Pearl Grey Cockerel, Pearl Grey Hen,
> Dilly Duck and Gaggly Goose,
> Goldfinch from the treetop.
> Come to Chick-Chick's wedding."

"Yes, you are invited. So come along with me." And off they walked.

After a while they met the goose. "Hello, dear Hen and friend Cockerel. Where are you going?" – "We are going to Chick-Chick's wedding." – "May I come too?" – "If you are invited you may." The cockerel unfolded the letter and read:

> "Pearl Grey Cockerel, Pearl Grey Hen,
> Dilly Duck and Gaggly Goose,
> Goldfinch from the treetop,
> Come to Chick-Chick's wedding."

"Yes, you are invited, so come along with us." And off they walked.

They met the duck. "Where are you going, dear Goose and Hen and Cockerel?" – "To Chick-Chick's wedding." – "May I come too?" – "Yes, if you are invited." The cockerel read:

> "Pearl Grey Cockerel, Pearl Grey Hen,
> Dilly Duck and Gaggly Goose,
> Goldfinch from the treetop,
> Come to Chick-Chick's wedding."

"Yes, you are invited. Come along."

Then they met the goldfinch. "Where are you going, dear friends Duck, Goose, Hen, and you, friend Cockerel?" – "To Chick-Chick's wedding." – "May I come along?" – "Sure, if you are invited." He opened the letter:

> "Pearl Grey Cockerel, Pearl Grey Hen,
> Dilly Duck and Gaggly Goose,
> Goldfinch from the treetop,
> Come to Chick-Chick's wedding."

"Hey, there you are as well." Then the five of them went on.

They met the wolf. The wolf also asked where they were going. "We are going to Chick-Chick's wedding," answered the cockerel. "Then I shall come too." – "You may, if you are invited." The cockerel read through the letter, but the wolf's name was not in it. "I still want to go," said the wolf. And because the others were afraid they answered: "Let us go then."

When they had walked a few steps the wolf said: "I am hungry. The cockerel answered: "I have not got anything for you." – "Then I will eat you." And the wolf opened his mouth and swallowed the cockerel, feathers and all.

A little further on the wolf again said: "I am hungry." The hen said: "I have not got anything for you." So the wolf ate her up as well.

A little further on the wolf again said: "I am hungry." The duck said: "I have not got anything for you." So the wolf ate her up as well.

A little further on the wolf said: "I am hungry." The goose said: "I have not got anything for you." And so the wolf ate her up as well.

Now the goldfinch and the wolf were the only ones left. The wolf said: "Dear Bird, I am hungry." – "And what would I have to give you? I have not got anything for you." – "Well then, I will eat you up." He opened his mouth . . . but . . . the bird hopped onto his head. The wolf did all he could to get hold of the goldfinch, but the bird hopped to and fro, flew up into the tree, hopped onto a branch, and flew back again, hopping from the wolf's head to his tail, making him furious.

When the wolf had tired himself out, the bird saw a woman. She was taking food to the mowers in the meadow. The goldfinch called to the wolf: "If you let me live I will see to it that you get a good meal, because the woman is taking spaghetti and meat to the mowers in the meadow. When she sees me she will want to catch me and then I shall fly from one branch to the other. She will put the basket down and you can eat everything."

And, indeed, when the woman saw the beautiful bird she came and stretched out her hand to catch it. But just then the goldfinch flew up. The woman put down the basket and ran after the bird. Then the wolf went to the basket and had a feast.

"Help! Help!" cried the woman. All the mowers came running, one with a sickle, another with a stick and they killed the wolf.

And out of the wolf's stomach jumped Gaggly Goose, Dilly Duck, Pearl Grey Hen and Pearl Grey Cockerel and together with Goldfinch they went to Chick-Chick's wedding.

From Holland

The Sparrow and the Blade of Grass

A sparrow once perched on a blade of grass and said to it: "Give me a swing, blade of grass." But the blade of grass answered: "No, I won't!"

So the sparrow flew off to the goat, and said to him: "Mr. Goat, Mr. Goat, go and eat the blade of grass. Because it won't give me a swing." But the goat answered: "No, I won't!"

So the sparrow flew off to the wolf and said to him: "Mr. Wolf, go and eat the goat! Because he won't go and eat the blade of grass, and the blade of grass won't give me a swing." But the wolf answered: "No, I won't!"

So the sparrow flew off to a man, and said to him: "Mr. Man, go and kill the wolf! Because he won't go and eat the goat, and the goat won't go and eat the blade of grass, and the blade of grass won't give me a swing." But the man answered: "No, I won't."

So the sparrow flew off to the fire, and said to it: "Fire, fire, go and burn the man! Because he won't go and kill the wolf, and the wolf won't go and eat the goat, and the goat won't go and eat the blade of grass, and the blade of grass won't give me a swing." But the fire answered: "No, I won't."

So the sparrow flew off to the water, and said to it: "Water, water, go and put out the fire! Because it won't go and burn the man, and the man won't go and kill the wolf, and the wolf won't go and eat the goat, and the goat won't go and eat the blade of grass, and the blade of grass won't give me a swing." But the water answered: "No, I won't."

So the sparrow flew off to the oxen, and said to them: "Oxen, oxen, go and drink up the water! Because it won't go and put out the fire, and the fire won't go and burn the man, and the man won't go and kill the wolf, and the wolf won't go and eat the goat, and the goat won't go and eat the blade of grass, and the blade of grass won't give me a swing."

Then the oxen went off to drink the water, and the water went off to put out the fire, and the fire went off to burn the man, and the man went off to kill the wolf, and the wolf went off to eat the goat, and the goat went off to eat the blade of grass, and the blade of grass got a terrible fright and said to the sparrow: "Sit down, I'll give you a swing." So the blade of grass started swinging the sparrow and singing:

> "Hushaby, baby, on the tree top,
> You'd better hold tight if you don't want to drop!"

From Russia

The Three Billy-Goats Gruff

Once upon a time there were three billy-goats who were on their way to the mountain grass to get fat and each of them was called Billy-Goat Gruff. On their way they had to cross a bridge over a waterfall and under the bridge lived a troll with eyes like pewter plates and a nose as long as a rake handle.

First came the youngest Billy-Goat Gruff. Trip, trap, trip, trap, went his hooves on the bridge. "Who's that trip-trapping over my bridge?" roared the troll.

"It is I, the smallest Billy-Goat Gruff, and I'm on my way to the mountain grass to get fat," said the billy-goat, in a tiny, tiny voice.

"Well, I am coming to eat you up!" said the troll.

"Oh no! Don't eat me up. I am only small. Wait a while till the second Billy-Goat Gruff comes, he is bigger than I am."

"Very well then," said the troll.

A little while later the second Billy-Goat Gruff came along.

Trot, trot, trot, trot, went his hooves on the bridge. "Who's that trot-trotting over my bridge?" roared the troll.

"It is I, the second Billy-Goat Gruff, on my way to the mountain grass to get fat," said the billy-goat in a clear, clear voice.

"Well, I am coming to eat you up!" said the troll.

"Oh no! Don't eat me up. Wait a while till the big Billy-Goat Gruff comes along. He is much bigger than I am."

"Very well then," said the troll.

By and by, the big Billy-Goat Gruff came along. Tramp, tramp, tramp, tramp, went his hooves on the bridge. "Who's that tramp-tramping over my bridge?" roared the troll.

"It is I, the big Billy-Goat Gruff!" said the billy-goat in a deep, deep voice.

"Well, I am coming to eat you up!" roared the troll.

"Up you come! I have two spears!
With them I'll tear your eyes and ears.
I have two mighty boulder-stones!
With them I'll crush your marrow and bones!"

said the billy-goat. And he charged at the troll and butted him over the edge of the waterfall. And then he went up to the mountain grass. There the billy-goats got so fat, that they could hardly walk home again. And as far as I know they are still as fat as that.

And this is the end of my tale.

From Norway

Goldilocks and the Three Bears

Once upon a time there were three bears, who lived together in a house in a wood. One of them was a great big bear, one was a middle-sized bear and one was a little tiny bear. They each had a bowl for their porridge: a great big bowl for the great big bear, a middle-sized bowl for the middle-sized bear and a little tiny bowl for the little tiny bear. They each had a chair to sit in: a great big chair for the great big bear, a middle-sized chair for the middle-sized bear, and a little tiny chair for the little tiny bear. And they each had a bed to sleep in: a great big bed for the great big bear, a middle-sized bed for the middle-sized bear and a little tiny bed for the little tiny bear.

One day they made the porridge for their breakfast and poured it into their porridge bowls. They saw that it was much too hot and would burn their mouths, so they went out for a walk in the woods whilst the porridge was cooling. They did not shut the door.

While they were out walking, a little girl came to their house. Her name was Goldilocks and she lived with her father and mother in a cottage at the edge of the wood. It was such a pleasant, sunny morning and all the bluebells were out in the wood, so she had gone for a walk before breakfast, and had lost her way among the trees.

Now she saw the house of the three bears, and went and knocked at the door. Nobody came to the door, so she peeped in. There was no one there and as she was tired and hungry she went into the house. There on the table were three bowls of porridge. She was so hungry that she could not help taking a spoon and tasting the porridge in the great big bowl of the great big bear but it was much too hot! So she took a spoon and tasted the porridge in the middle-sized bowl of the middle-sized bear but it was much too cold! So Goldilocks took a spoon and tasted the porridge in the little tiny bowl of the little tiny bear. This time it was neither too hot nor too cold; it was just right! So Goldilocks, being hungry, could not help eating it all up.

Then, feeling tired, and as there was no one to ask, Goldilocks sat down on the great big bear's great big chair.

But it was much too hard! So she sat down on the middle-sized chair of the middle-sized bear. It was much too soft and she sank right down into the straw seat. Then she sat down on the little tiny bear's little tiny chair. It was neither too hard nor too soft; it was just right. So she settled herself in it and there she sat until the bottom of the chair fell out, and down she went, 'plonk' upon the ground.

Then she thought she would go upstairs and see if there was anyone there. But at the top of the stairs she saw no one, only three beds.

Being tired, she could not help lying down on the great big bear's great big bed, but it was too high for her at the head! So she lay down on the middle-sized bear's middle-sized bed. But it was too high for her at the feet! So Goldilocks lay down on the little tiny bear's little tiny bed. And it was neither too high at the head nor too high at the feet; it was just right! So she covered herself up comfortably and lay there until she fell fast asleep.

Now the three bears said: "Our porridge will be cool enough." They came home to their house. There on the table were their porridge bowls.

The great big bear said, in his great, big, rough, gruff voice: "Somebody has been eating my porridge!"

Then the middle-sized bear with her growly middle-sized voice said: "Somebody has been eating my porridge!"

Then the little tiny bear in his wee little shrill voice called out: "Somebody has been eating my porridge and has eaten it all up!" So the great big bear and the middle-sized bear each gave the little tiny bear some of their porridge.

Then they looked at their seats. The great big bear said, in his great, big, rough, gruff voice: "Somebody has been sitting on my chair."

Then the middle-sized bear in her growly, middle-sized voice said: "Somebody has been sitting on my chair."

And then the little tiny bear in his wee little shrill voice called out: "Somebody has been sitting on my chair and has sat the bottom out of it."

But the great big bear said: "Never mind, I'll mend it for you."

Then the three bears went upstairs and looked at their beds. The great big bear said, in his great, big, rough gruff voice: "Somebody has been lying on my bed."

Then the middle-sized bear in her growly, middle-sized voice said: "Somebody has been lying on my bed."

And then the little tiny bear called out in his wee little shrill voice: "Somebody has been lying on my bed – and here she is!" And there she was with her shining hair spread out over the little tiny bear's pillow.

Goldilocks had been so fast asleep that she had not heard the loud and deep voices of the bigger bears. But when the little tiny bear called out in his wee little shrill voice she woke up straight away.

She sat up and saw the bright brown eyes of the three bears fixed on her in astonishment. It gave her such a fright that she jumped up and ran down the stairs and out into the wood as fast as she could go, and soon she was safe home in her father's and mother's cottage.

And the three bears went on living in their house in the wood and no one ever troubled them again.

From Russia

1. Run, Goldilocks, run,
   Out into the sun!
   Here comes little baby bear,
   You broke his little baby chair.
   Run, Goldilocks, run.

2. Run, Goldilocks, run,
   Out into the sun!
   The woods are behind you.
   The bears cannot find you.
   Run, Goldilocks, run.

L. Charter

Recommended Reading

A is for Ox, B. Sanders ISBN 0 679 74285 9 Vintage Books

Failure to Connect, J. Healy ISBN 0 684 85539 9 Simon & Schuster

Set Free Childhood, M. Large. ISBN 1 903458 43 9 Hawthorn Press

Rudolf Steiner - Life, work, inner path and social intentions, R. Lissau
ISBN 1 869890 06 X Hawthorn Press

Lifeways, G. Davy & B. Voors ISBN 0 950706 24 8 Hawthorn Press

The Spiritual Tasks of the Homemaker, M. Schmidt-Brabant
ISBN 0 904693 84 8 Temple Lodge Press, England

Education Towards Freedom ISBN 0 906155 32 0 Lanthorn Press, England

Work and Play in Early Childhood, F. Jaffke
ISBN 0 86315 227 9 Floris Books, Edinburgh, Scotland

Festivals, Family and Food, D. Carey & J. Large
ISBN 1 950706 23 X Hawthron Press

Festivals Together, S. Fitzjohn, M. Weston & J. Large
ISBN 1 869890 46 9 Hawthorn Press

Understanding Children's Drawings, M. Strauss
Rudolf Steiner Press, England

The Wisdom of Fairytales, R. Meyer ISBN 0 86315 208 2 Floris Books

A Guide to Child Health, M. Glöckler & W. Goebel
ISBN 0 86315 390 9 Floris Books

Education as Preventive Medicine – A Salutogenic Approach,
M Glöckler ISBN 0 945803 63 X Rudolf Steiner College Press, USA.

Between Form and Freedom, B Staley ISBN 1 869890 08 6 Hawthorn Press

Brothers and Sisters, K. König ISBN 0 86315 446 8 Floris Books

The Challenge of the Will, Margret Meyerkort & Rudi Lissau
ISBN 0 945803 41 9 Rudolf Steiner College Press, California, USA

The Oxford Nursery Songbook,
ISBN 0 19 330193 8 Oxford University Press

The Oxford Dictionary of Nursery Rhymes
ISBN 0 19 860088 7 Oxford University Press

Let us Form a Ring, Acorn Hill Children's Centre,
Silver Spring, MD, USA

The Book of 1000 Poems ISBN 0 00 185508 5 Collins Educational

English Fairy Tales, J. Jacobs ISBN 0 679 42809 7 Everyman's Library

The Complete Grimm's Fairy Tales ISBN 0 394 70930 6 Pantheon Books

Milly Molly Mandy Books, J. Brisley, Puffin Books

Seven-Year-Old Wonder Book, I. Wyatt ISBN 0 86315 527 8 Floris Books

Acknowledgements

Further to the acknowledgement on page 3 of this book, the following is a list of permissions granted to reproduce previously published copyright material. Where it has not been possible to locate the original copyright holder, we tender our apologies to any owner whose rights may have been unwittingly infringed.

From HarperCollins Publishers Ltd, we are grateful to reproduce the following items from The Book of 1000 Poems: *King Winter sat on his throne one day – titled Outside –* by Hugh Chesterman; *I have heard a mother bird singing in the rain – titled Welcome to Spring –* by Irene Thompson; *Buttercups and daisies* by Mary Howitt, and *A farmer once planted some little brown seeds – titled A Growing Rhyme –* by J. M. Westrup. *I have made a pretty nest,* words by Ann Elliott and reprinted from Fingers and Thumbs, copyright 1933, Stainer & Bell Ltd, London. *Mother Earth,* music by E. Lebret and reproduced by kind permission of E. Lebret and the Waldorf School Association of Ontario, Inc. *The Sparrow and the Blade of Grass* from More Russian Picture Tales by Valery Carrick, translated by Nevill Forbes, published by Dover Publications, Inc., Mineola, N.Y. U.S.A., and reproduced here with the kind assistance of Dover Publications, Inc.

Wynstones Press

Wynstones Press publishes and distributes a range of books, including many titles for children, parents and teachers.

Also available is a wide selection of postcards, folded cards and prints reproduced from original work by a variety of artists. Included amongst these are many works by David Newbatt, who illustrated the covers for this book.

Wynstones Press also distributes a selection of beautifully illustrated Advent Calendars, from publishers in Europe.

For further information please contact:

Wynstones Press
Ruskin Glass Centre
Wollaston Road
Stourbridge
West Midlands DY8 4HE.
England.

Telephone: +44 (0) 1384 399455
Email: info@wynstonespress.com
Website: wynstonespress.com